Wendy Whale

HAPPY READING!

This book is especially for:

_____

Suzanne Tate
Author—
brings fun and
facts to us in her
Nature Series.

James Melvin
Illustrator—
brings joyous life
to Suzanne Tate's
characters.

Author Suzanne Tate
and
Illustrator James Melvin

Wendy Whale

A Tale of a Huge Creature

Suzanne Tate

Illustrated by James Melvin

Nags Head Art

To Educators Everywhere
who teach us to be good stewards
of earth's creatures

Library of Congress Control Number 2014900498
ISBN 978-1-878405-62-3
ISBN 1-878405-62-4
Published by
Nags Head Art, Inc., P.O. Box 2149, Manteo, NC 27954
Copyright© 2014 by Nags Head Art, Inc.

Wendy Whale had a big head
and giant jaws.

She was a huge mammal
swimming in the sea.

Rough white patches were
on her head.

Whale lice lived on the patches!
They were tiny shrimp-like
animals hitching a ride.

Wendy Whale had two blowholes
on top of her head.

It was easy to spot her
V-shaped blow.

HUMANS who study whales
said she was a "true" whale.

Wendy wasn't like a killer whale.
She had no teeth and
didn't eat fish!

Most of the time, Wendy ate plankton
— little animals living in the sea.

baleen

Her giant jaws were special!
Like other true whales, her upper jaw was fitted
with plates of baleen.

The baleen plates were bristly.
With the bristles, Wendy could strain tiny animals
from the water when she was feeding.

After she strained a mouthful of prey,
Wendy pushed the water out, dived,
and swallowed the food.

Wendy Whale was a mother whale.
She had a big calf that lived
and swam beside her.

The calf — Winnie — could not live
without milk from her mother.

Wendy Whale and her calf swam
and swam every day.

They had large fins like paddles
and big tails to propel themselves.

The huge mother whale had to eat
constantly to live and feed her calf.
She ate tons of food every day!

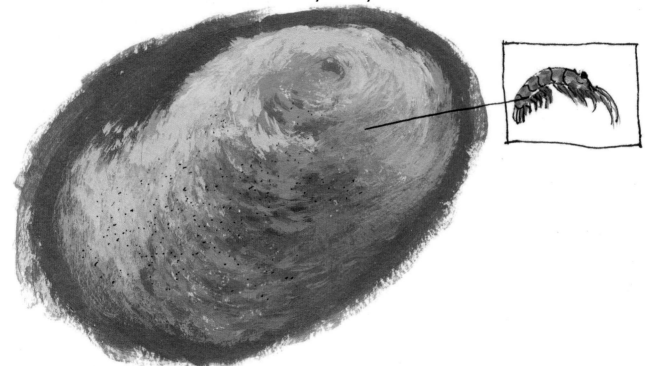

Sometimes, Wendy would find "clouds" of krill
to strain and eat. They were tiny shrimp-like
animals swirling up from the bottom of the sea.

Winnie Whale wondered one day —
"What kind of whale are we?"
She swam up close to her big mother to ask.

"We are called right whales,"
Wendy replied.
"Why is that?" Winnie asked.

"It's a sad story — but I will tell you.
Years ago, men in boats came after us,"
her mother said.

"They hunted and harvested
whales to sell."

"The hunters thought we were the "right" whale or best one to catch," she went on, "because they could make a lot of money with our kind of whale."

"Oh, my, do we still have to worry about that?" Winnie asked.

"No, we don't," her mother replied. "HELPFUL HUMANS now protect us, and the whale hunters stay away."

"That's good!" Winnie said. "Then we don't have anything to worry about now?"

"Whales always have to be careful,"
Wendy replied.

"We need to stay away from big ships
and watch where we swim."

One day, Winnie swam a little way
away from her mother's side.

She didn't see a big ship.
that was coming close to her.

"Quick! Swim here to me," Wendy cried.
Winnie listened to her mother
and swam toward her.

The ship sailed on, and Winnie
escaped danger!

Winnie was surprised to see another
young whale swimming alone.

"What are you doing here by yourself?"
Winnie asked as she swam near the calf.
He was about the same size as she.

"A big ship came close to my mother and me," the young male said. "Now I can't find her."

Winnie knew that he must be

"Maybe my mother can take care of you
as she does me," Winnie said.
"Let's ask her."

When asked, the whale mother was worried to think
of caring for two calves.

"It is a big task for me to care for you,"
Wendy Whale said.
And she rolled and turned away
from the new calf.

But he was starving and kept trying
to nurse the big mother whale!

At last, Wendy felt sad
for the baby whale.
She let him get milk
from her.

Winnie Whale was happy!
She had a new brother.

The calves began to play
with each other.

"He really is the right whale for us," Winnie thought.
"I'm glad my mother has been able to help him."

"Let's keep moving!" her mother said.
"I need to look for even more food."

And the three right whales swam
away together — a happy new family
in the sea!